BASSLINES

BY JOE HUBBARD

AMSCO PUBLICATIONS
London/New York/Sydney

Exclusive Distributors:
MUSIC SALES LIMITED
8/9 Frith Street, London, W1V 5TZ, England
MUSIC SALES PTY. LIMITED
120 Rothschild Avenue, Rosebery, NSW 2018, Australia

This book © Copyright 1985 by Amsco Publications
ISBN 0.7119.0622.X
Order No. AM38795

Designed and art directed by Mike Bell
Cover photograph by Francis Lumley
Cover photograph retouching by Nick Whitaker
Arranged by Joe Hubbard
Engraved by Musicprint
Typeset by Futurafoto in Gill Light, Gill Bold and Century Old Style

Music Sales complete catalogue lists thousands of titles and is free
from your local music book shop, or direct from Music Sales Limited.
Please send a cheque/postal order for £1.50 for postage to
Music Sales Limited, 8/9 Frith Street, London, W1V 5TZ.

Printed in England by JB Offset Printers (Marks Tey) Limited, Marks Tey, Essex.

INTRODUCTION

To understand the music in this book and how to use it,
I will give you a general idea of why I wrote it.

In the seven years I have been playing, I have noticed the lack of
good books about the bass guitar on the market.
Mostly it is flooded with elementary method books with
poor explanations of what they are trying to teach.
Apart from one book entitled 'Slap It', I have not seen any covering
the slap style, which is becoming the most prominent style in music today.
So instead of writing yet another method book on this style,
I thought it would be more beneficial to write a book transcribing and
analysing bass parts from some of the best bass players in the world.

HERE'S SOME ADVICE

1. Read through these lines very slowly, the mind will take in
the music correctly this way. Trying to play things too fast at first will lead to
mistakes and later must be re-learned.

2. If you don't have the recordings on which these pieces have been played,
please get them so you can play along with them.

3. Once you've learnt these lines, transpose them into other keys.
This will enable you to use them in other situations.

4. **Remember to be patient,** the players who are written about in this book
didn't learn to play overnight.
Each person grows at their own rate – so relax and enjoy the music.

SYMBOLS

THE DEADEN NOTE
The deaden note adds rhythmical content to the slap style but has no pitch.
To do this, you play what is written and damp the note with the left hand where the x's are written.

THE VIBRATO
This is usually done with the 3rd finger. You push the string up and pull it back in
a quick succession across the finger board.

HARMONIC
The diamond shaped symbol means the note is struck as a harmonic.

MARK KING

Mark King was born on October 20, 1958, at Cowes on the Isle Of Wight and he started playing drums when he was nine years old. It was not until his arrival in London at the age of 19 that he took up the bass guitar; initially he worked in a Charing Cross Road musical instrument shop selling bass guitars.

In order to obtain the position he had been obliged to lie about his bass playing ability. In a matter of weeks he had mastered the instrument and developed the thumb style for which he would become widely admired.

King was already familiar with the Gould brothers – Boon and Phil – from his years on the Isle Of Wight and in 1980 this trio, plus keyboard player Mike Lindup, formed Level 42. All four had an affinity with jazz artists like Miles Davis, John McLaughlin, Keith Jarrett and Jan Hammer.

Level 42's recording debut came via the independent Elite Records label in May of 1980. A major recording contract with Polydor followed almost immediately and the group have since recorded four further LP's and a clutch of impressive singles including the top ten hit "Sun Goes Down (Living It Up)."

THE CHINESE WAY

MARK KING, PHILIP GOULD & WALIOU BADAROU

Well, let's face it. We've all been influenced by other players. This is a great example of being influenced by Jaco with a very sixteenth staccato and busy line in the main verse. Notice in Section B the line becomes very sparse, thus creating tension and making the line in Section A that more effective.

(Remember Mark's not just jamming along here. He's created an actual arrangement. Notice every section has a stylistic change to complement the previous section. That is the golden rule when playing on a tune). Notice on Section D the line becomes sparse again, sometimes less is more! Again, using 5ths and 4ths with power chord effect. Practise this one very slowly and gradually build up speed to get articulation perfect. This one is played with fingers.

DUNE TUNE

MARK KING

This is a great tune showing how the role of the bass has changed over the last ten years. Not only is he playing the melody but by combining double stops (two notes being played at once), gives the effect of those old jazz chord melodies played by Joe Pass and George Benson. I suggest you learn Sections A, B and C by learning the top line first, then combining with the lower parts. You could even get together with another bass player and play these sections in duet form. The entire piece is played with fingers except Section F which is slapped, incorporating the use of 5ths giving a rock power chord effect.

THE SUN GOES DOWN
LIVING IT UP

MARK KING, MICHAEL LINDUP, PHILIP GOULD & WALIOU BADAROU

The tune is great – what a great bass line! The intro being very sparse, leaves lots of room to let the groove build. The line on Section A is very laid back and played very short and staccato.

The line on Section B is a little bit busier, leading back into the same groove that's on the intro. Again, this one is played with fingers. Who said Mark King can only slap?

HEATHROW

WALIOU BADAROU

This groove is a funk shuffle feel. The eighth notes are sort of played as swing eights.

turned around.
"Lopsy Lu" was

The basic line in the intro and section A is a nice pattern to use in other tunes similar to this. As a matter of fact, I'm sure Mark got this idea from a Stanley Clarke tune entitled "Lopsy Lu" off Stanley's second solo album. It's exactly the same except

The entire tune is slapped, and remember the deadened notes are very important. They give the percussiveness which plays a big role in Mark's playing.

STANLEY CLARKE

Stanley Clarke was born on June 30, 1951, and steeped in music from an early age. His first instruments were the violin and 'cello and at 13 he took up the classical double bass. He studied classical music at the Philadelphia Music Academy and it was here that he was also introduced to rock, jazz and soul.

In 1970 Clarke abandoned his studies and joined Horace Silver's group. On leaving Silver he teamed up with Joe Henderson's Band where he met keyboards player Chick Corea. Soon Clarke and Corea combined their talents in the influential fusion group Return To Forever which also included Lenny White on drums and a number of first-rate guitarists, among them Al Di Meola.

Return To Forever made seven albums while they remained together, and Clarke also appeared (either live or on record) with Pharaoh Saunders, Stan Getz, Carlos Santana, Dexter Gordon, Art Blakey, Aretha Franklin and The Barbarians, a Rolling Stones spin-off band featuring Ron Wood and Keith Richards.

Clarke also recorded a number of solo albums using his Return To Forever colleagues. These include his 1974 debut "Stanley Clarke," "Journey To Love" (1975) and "I Wanna Play For You" (1979). More recently Clarke has performed with George Duke and Lenny White.

HOT FUN

STANLEY CLARKE

This song is very fast and funky and displays the chops that Stanley has. The line–on Section A, the symbols over the deadened notes (IOIOIO) mean 'In Out' which means he puts his thumb in through the string and pulls it back out, thus getting that effect at such speed. This line recurs in several spots and is articulated the same every time. The second part of Section A is yet another fine example of using double stops to create a fuller and bigger sound. This tune is slapped.

SILLY PUTTY

STANLEY CLARKE

Here comes a difficult one! Starting with the intro using a kind of chord melody style, pulling the melody part with his fingers, hitting the low notes with his thumb. And in the 5th bar of the intro, the bend is done playing the open G string and, with the left hand index finger, depressing the G string above the nut, making the note bend to G#.

The line at Section A is slapped and remember to articulate the deadened notes properly. Section B is slapped, much more sparse than Section A. The bend in the 6th bar is done in the same way as before. Strike the D harmonic on the 7th fret on the G string and, with the left hand index finger, depress the G string above the nut. In Section F, which is the solo, he starts off using

percussive and melodic attack almost as if he's accompanying his own solo. Notice in the 6th bar where I've written

This means he's playing 6 32nd notes in the place of 4. Also notice the last bar in Section I. Stanley's bass goes up an octave above the G on the 12th fret of the G string. Most conventional basses don't go that high. Take your time and good luck!

BEND

[I]

[J]

Fine

SONG TO JOHN PART II

STANLEY CLARKE

This song is a good example of where the bass plays the melody. On the record, he plays it on the acoustic bass so this one would be nice done on your fretless. (You don't have one? Well, get one!) There are some nice interval jumps on this one and it gets quite high in spots. The feel is a jazz samba. Practise slowly and remember, be patient! Your assignment on this is to record the chord changes on Section B and practise improvising a solo over and over and over and …

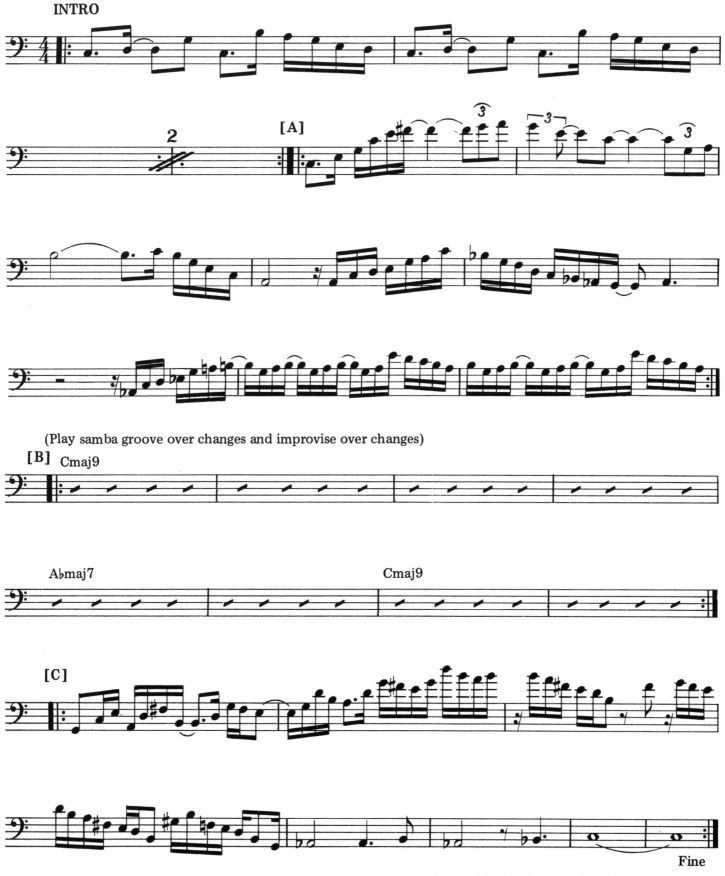

(Play samba groove over changes and improvise over changes)

THE DANCER

STANLEY CLARKE

I chose this one because you rarely hear slapping on a Brazilian or Latin type groove. Well, here it is, folks. Very simple but very effective. Try and investigate other Latin styles and utilize slapping in them.

MARCUS MILLER

Marcus Miller was born in Brooklyn, New York, in 1961 and he inherited a family tradition of musical prowess. His father played jazz keyboards and his second cousin, Wynton Kelly, played piano with Miles Davis during the fifties. His earliest musical memories are picking out tunes on the family piano and learning the clarinet at the age of 10.

Miller was nothing if not eclectic. By the age of 15 he had mastered the piano, clarinet, bass guitar and saxophone, and was also a blossoming vocalist. His first professional work – at 15 – was with a New York band called Harlem River Drive who mixed jazz and r&b covers, and he became known locally for joining in jam sessions in a park in Jamaica, Queens.

In 1977 Miller was hired as bassist with jazz flautist Bobbi Humphreys and he simultaneously contributed material to pianist Lonnie Liston Smith's "Love Land" album. After a year with Humphreys he toured with Lenny White then distinguished

himself on the New York session scene. Among those who used Miller in the studio were Miles Davis, Roberta Flack, Aretha Franklin, Elton John, Luther Vandross, Grover Washington Jnr., Tom Browne, Dave Grusin and Bob James. His relationship with Miles Davis was cemented with a year and a half as bassist for the legendary trumpeter.

In 1982 Miller could be found playing with the *Saturday Night Live* house band where he met saxophonist David Sanborn. The pair collaborated on Sanborn's "Voyeur" album and the same year Miller began work on his own début album "Suddenly".

Between the release of that album and Miller's recently issued eponymously titled follow-up, the now renowned bassist worked closely with Luther Vandross. They penned material together for Teddy Pendergrass, Dionne Warwick and Aretha Franklin including the latter's 1983 hit "Jump To It".

RIO FUNK

LEE RITENOUR

The reason I liked this one so much is because of the varied sectional changes and the amazing slapping solo he plays. The intro starts off with very syncopated rhythmical ideas.

Section A still deals with the syncopation but somewhat more simplistic in structure.

Section B goes into a samba feel, but notice he doesn't play the typical root 5th type line. Good luck on Section C because this is quite advanced and sophisticated rhythmically. The last beat in the 2nd bar I've written

which means there are 5 16ths in the place of 4 16ths. In Section D notice the nice embellishment in the 6th bar (an old blues lick but it just might work). The whole tune is slapped, except for the samba sections.

[B]
(Samba feel)

To Coda ⊕

[E]

[F]

Fine

RAG BAG

DAVE GRUSIN

I'd really like to hear how the title to this song came about. Anyway, the intro starts out very sparse, just hitting the accents with the drummer. The 8-bar drum fill leads nicely into Section A.

This section is slapped. Remember, articulate those deadened notes properly! Section B is played with fingers, a nice straight groove to complement the previous section. Notice in the 9th bar of Section B, the 6/4 bar. Don't freak out – just count to six. As the piece carries on, it's pretty straight ahead to the rest of the tune. Remember, this is a groove tune – make it groove. A lot of guys can't groove. They just want to be flash. It's just as important to play a solid groove for seven minutes as it is to play a fast solo!!

[E]

Fine

RUN FOR COVER

MARCUS MILLER

This is for all you funkateers out there funkin' for the real thrill! No, but seriously, folks, this one is nice. Slapped throughout, including the 16 bar solo at Section D. The thing to notice is how he effectively takes the idea at the intro and embellishes it at letters A and C. It's such a good example of just slightly changing around a certain pattern – and so musical. At the 5th and 6th bar of Section D the harmonics are played with fingers. So practise this because you'll be switching from fingers to slap quite fast.

COULD IT BE YOU

MARCUS MILLER

This is another fine example of the bass playing the melody. Yes, that's right – get your fretless out again. (Come on, man, I told you to get one). It pretty much remains in the high register throughout. Watch for the 2/4 bar in the intro and Sections B and D. On the record after this melody is played, he takes a solo. Your homework is to transcribe that solo and study it. Also, try making up your own solo as well.

JACO PASTORIUS

Jaco Pastorius was born in Philadelphia on December 1, 1951, but he grew up in Florida where he began an early career as a drummer. It was a football injury that led to him taking up the bass and he initially moulded his style on the soul music of James Brown and the Stax records label. It was not long before he advanced to jazz, taking in Charlie Parker, John Coltrane, Miles Davis and Wes Montgomery along with leading performers in Cuban calypso music.

In 1971 Pastorius joined his first band, Wayne Cochran and the CC Riders, who concentrated on r&b. Shortly afterwards he played with the Ira Sullivan Quartet, Pat Metheny and Bob Moses, and Paul Bley. At the same time he performed in a Fort Lauderdale club called Bachelors III, backing up touring artists like Nancy Wilson, The Four Seasons, The Temptations, The Supremes and Della Reese.

It was Bobby Colomby, the drummer with Blood, Sweat and

Tears, who brought Pastorius to Epic Records in 1975 to record his first solo LP. At the same time he collaborated with Ian Hunter on the latter's "All American Alien Boy" album.

In 1976 Pastorius replaced Alphonzo Johnson in Weather Report and quickly assumed a pre-eminent position in the group beside keyboards player Joe Zawinul and reeds player Wayne Shorter. His work on the group's "Heavy Weather" LP was widely acclaimed and his name can now be found on the credits for seven Weather Report LP's.

More recently Pastorius has released a second solo LP titled "Word Of Mouth" and toured with his own sextet. For a period he continued as a casual member of Weather Report but he now juggles his creative endeavours between his own solo projects and session work for a galaxy of talented performers.

COME ON, COME OVER

JACO PASTORIUS & B. HERZOG

This one is from Jaco's first album entitled "Jaco Pastorius" on Epic Records. I remember when this album first came out in 1976. No-one had heard anything like it before and he became the most talked about bass player around. This album was nominated for two Grammy Awards and shortly after he was asked to join the famous Weather Report. He was the first person to play fretless bass in the way that he does. As a matter of fact, it's hard not to sound like him when you pick up a fretless.

Anyway, this tune displays Jaco's lightning flash style of funk. The intro starts off with a nice blues lick, leading into Section A which he leaves quite sparse, setting up the second part of Section A when he really takes off. Notice how he uses deadened notes with the finger style of playing. Make sure you transpose these licks in other keys. They're great funk licks!

Repeat [B] and fade

TEEN TOWN

JACO PASTORIUS

This tune is a study in itself for any bass player. He plays the melody and it's one of the most musical pieces for bass I've ever heard. Jaco also plays great drums on this tune. Watch out for all the accents and articulations I've written in. Also, the key change at Section C which remains for the rest of the tune. Good luck with this one. You'll be proud of yourself when you get it down.

RIVER PEOPLE

JACO PASTORIUS

This is a very ethnic sounding tune. Of course – Jaco hailing from Florida – there's loads of rivers and swamp lands down there. The bass line here is very hypnotic and flowing – like a river. I love the way he plays around with the main idea just changing the notes around here and there. Notice when you take the repeat on the 1st ending, go back to the intro but no repeat on intro. Notice on Section D the line is played one octave above where it's written.

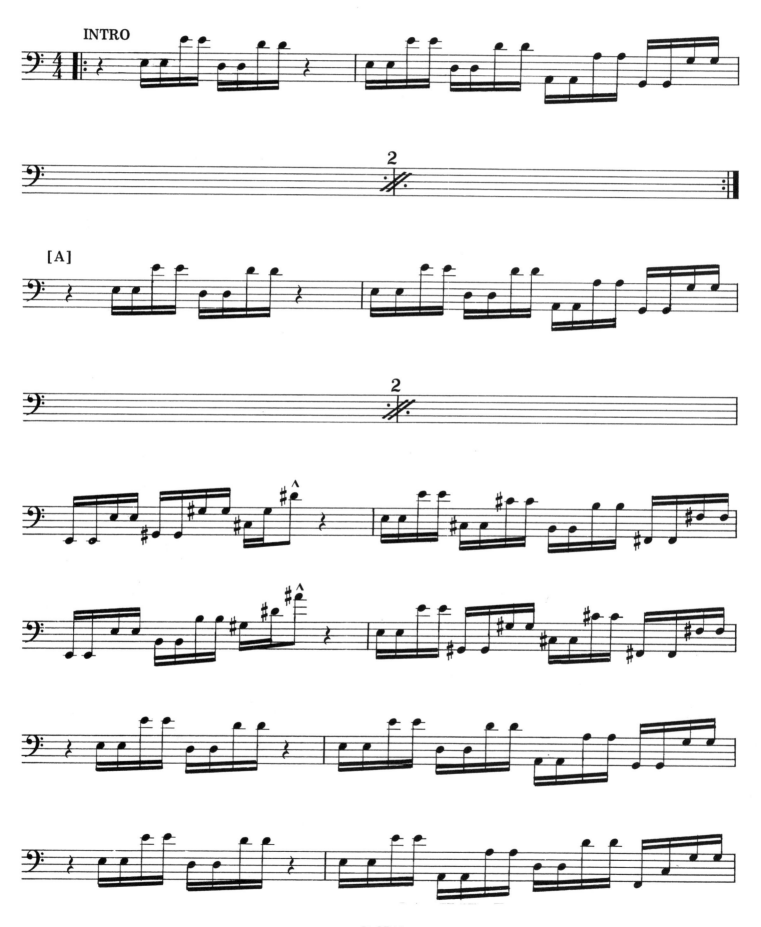

CHROMATIC FANTASY

J. S. BACH. ARRANGED BY JACO PASTORIUS

This is for those chosen few who managed to get to the end of the book. I thought I'd leave you with something you'd remember for a while, and believe me, if you get this together, you'll remember it! It's by Johann Sebastian Bach, and a good rendition of this famous classic. All I can say is, "Good Luck," and practise hard. Watch for the parts played up the octave and hey, hey, hey, let's be careful out there!!

JOE HUBBARD

Was born in the United States on June 16, 1957.
He studied 3½ years at Berklee College of Music in Boston.
Has played and recorded with such artists as Gary Numan, Petula Clark,
Mose Allison, Morrisey and Mullen, Bill Sharp, along with various
sessions ranging from jingles to film soundtracks.
Formerly the resident bassist with the "Morrisey Mullen Band."
Also leader of jazz funk band "Hubbard's Cubbard" with one album to date.

BIBLIOGRAPHY

I've provided a list of books here that have helped me develop my musical life.
Some of these books may help you understand more about my book and help your
musical development grow to the fullest.

Artful Arpeggios
by Don Mock
Published by REH

Hot Licks
by Don Mock
Published by REH

20th Century Intervallic Designs
by Joe Dorio
Published by REH

Fusion
by Joe Dorio
Published by Dale Zdenek

Thesaurus of Scales and Melodic Patterns
by Nicolas Slonimsky (very advanced)
Published by Charles Scribner's Sons

Bach Cello Suite
by J.S. Bach
Published by G. Schirmer

Harmonics for Electric Bass
by Adam Novick
Published by Amsco Publications

Jazz Improvisation
by David Baker
Published by DB Music Workshop

Develop Sight Reading
by Gaston Dufrene
Published by Charles Colin Publisher

Contemporary Etudes for Bass Clef
by Alan Colin
Published by Charles Colin

Advanced Jazz Rock Rhythms
by David Chesky
Published by Charles Colin

Modern Reading Text in 4/4 Time
by Louis Benson
Published by Belwin Mills

Odd Time Reading Text
by Louis Benson
Published by Belwin Mills

Chord Studies For Trombone
by Joe Viola
Published by Berklee Press

Slap It
by Tony Oppenheim
Published by Theodore Presser Company

Charlie Parker Omni Book
by Jamey Aebersold
Published by Atlantic Music Corp.

Thumb Basics
by Jonas Hellborg
Published by Amsco Publications

I would like to thank all the people who made this project possible:
Peter Evans, Kevin Gould, Jim Mullen, Dick Morrisey, Neal Wilkinson for
helping me with some rhythms. Special thanks to Mark King for giving some of
his time and to the rest of the players in the book.
Chris Charlesworth for his excellent biographies.
Great thanks to all my mentors, Flip Nuñez (I love you man!),
John Neves, Rich Appleman and Jeff Berlin.
Many thanks to my parents and most of all to my wife, Penny, who had to
endure all my craziness throughout this project.

1/94 (17079)